Mosaic Coloring Fun

Space

& Other Cool Stuff

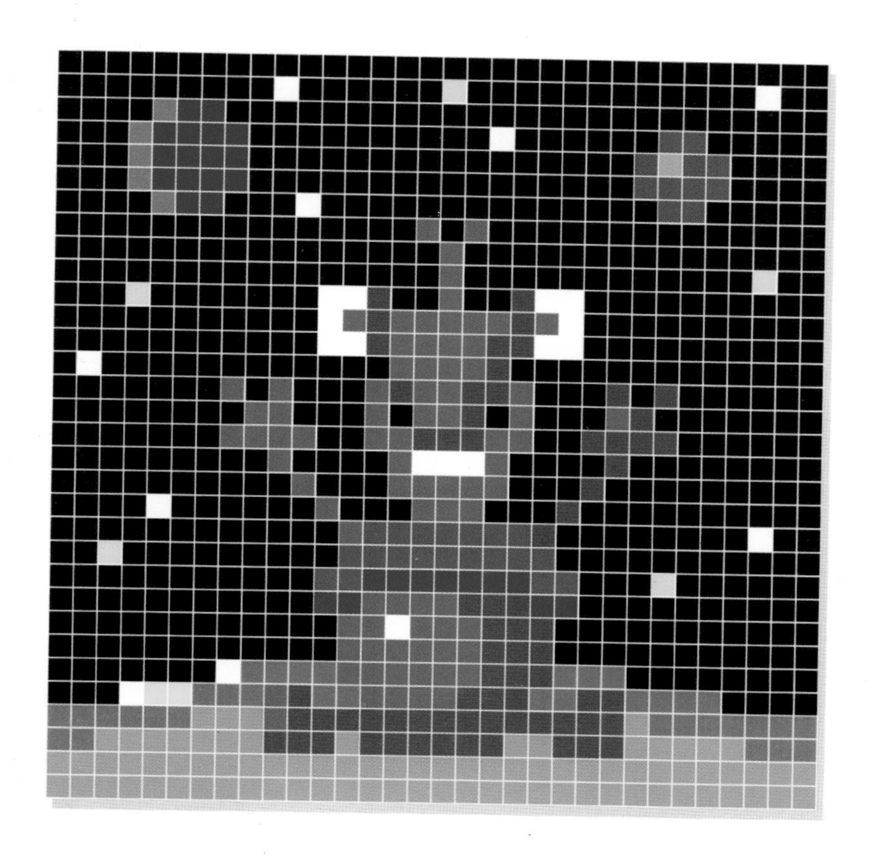

Licensed exclusively to Top That Publishing Ltd
Tide Mill Way, Woodbridge, Suffolk, IP12 1AP, UK
www.topthatpublishing.com

0 2 4 6 8 9 7 5 3 1
Printed and bound in China

Raging Rocket!

Copy this speedy space explorer, blasting through the universe!

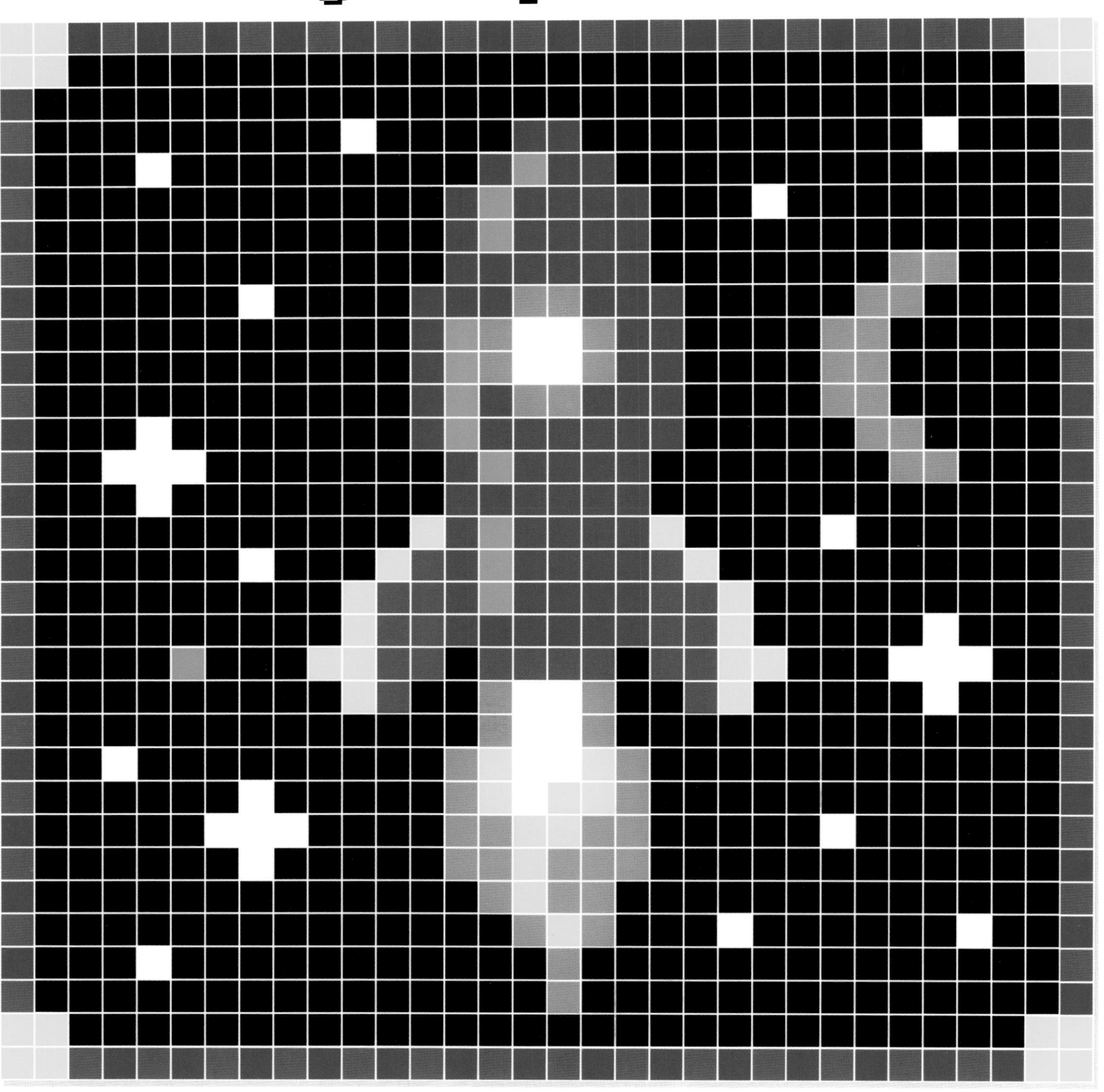

Now it's your turn!

Color in the grid below by copying the picture of the rocket on the left!

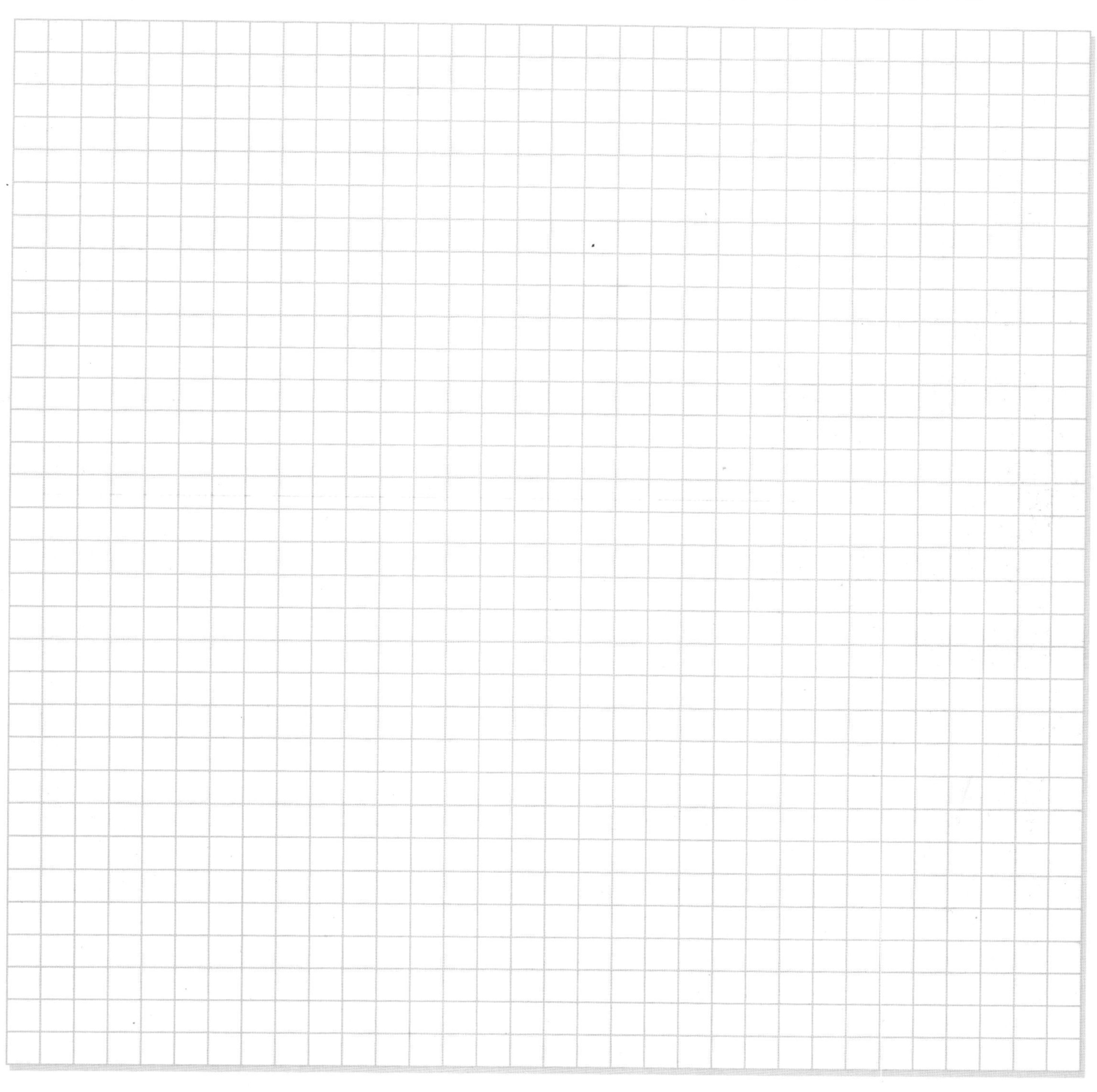

Splish, Splash!

Copy this splashing schoolgirl playing in the puddles!

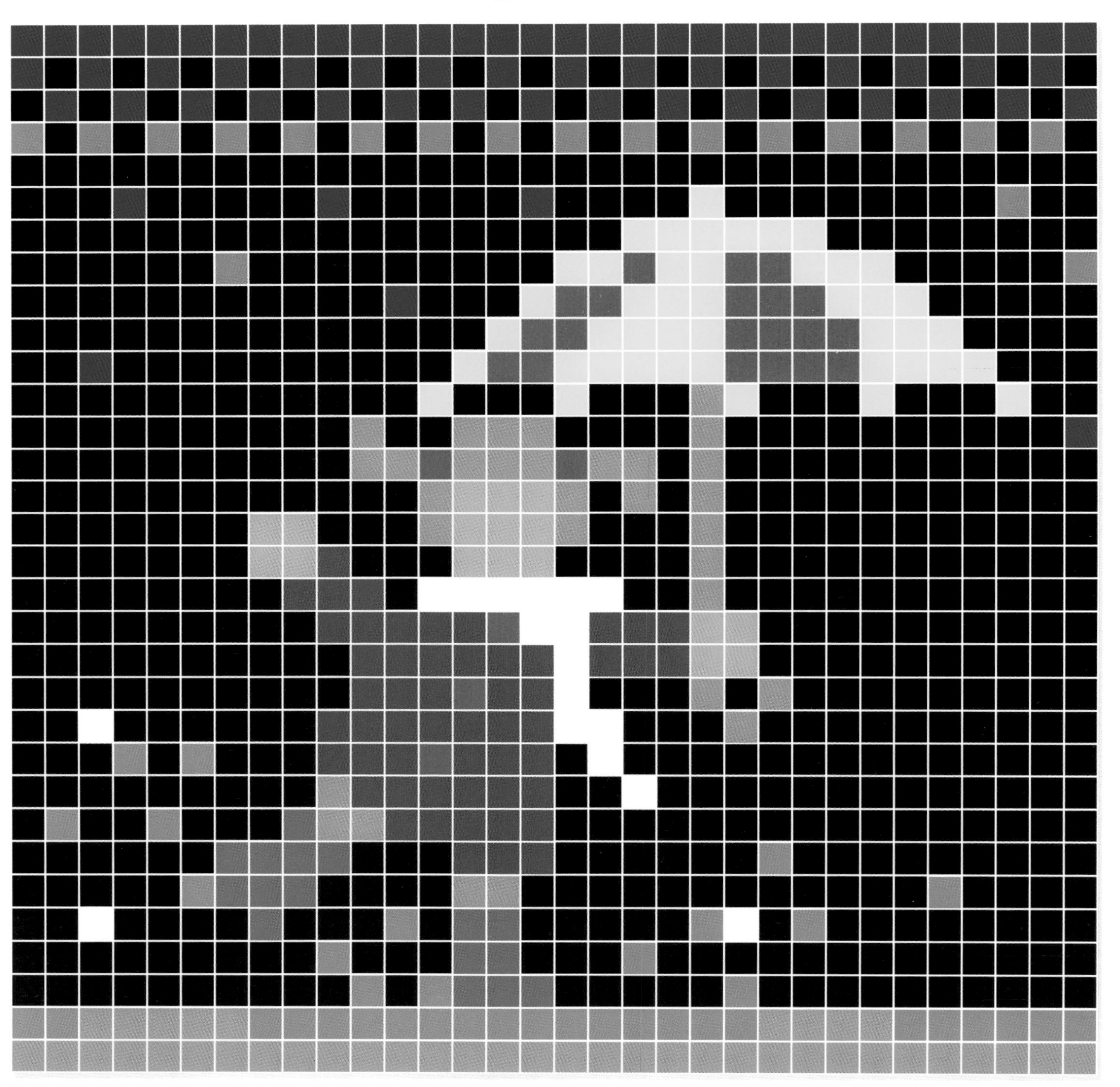

Now it's your turn!

Color in the grid below by copying the picture of the schoolgirl on the left!

Soccer Skills!

Are you quick enough to copy this speedy soccer player?

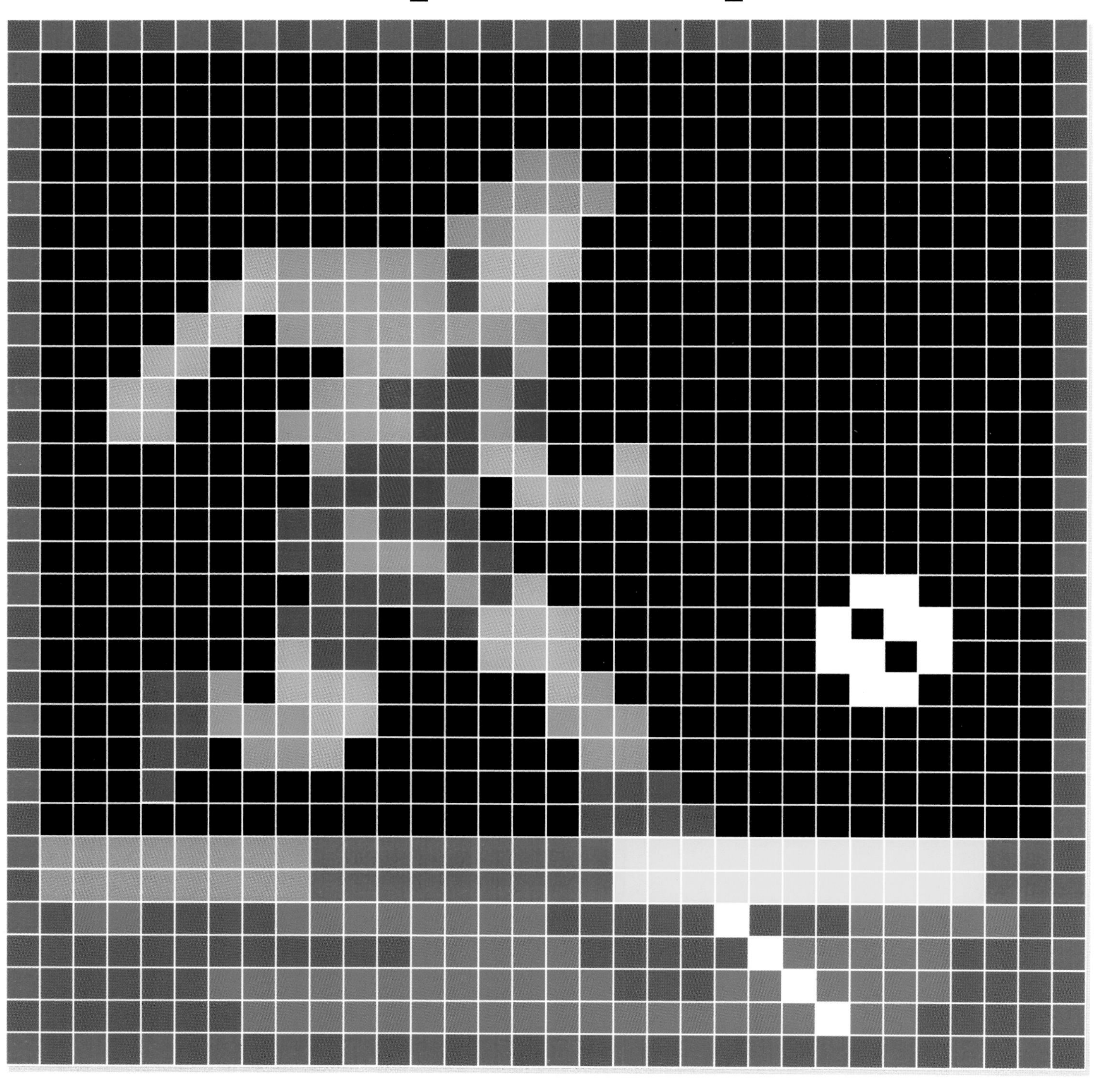

Now it's your turn!

Color in the grid below by copying the picture of the soccer player on the left!

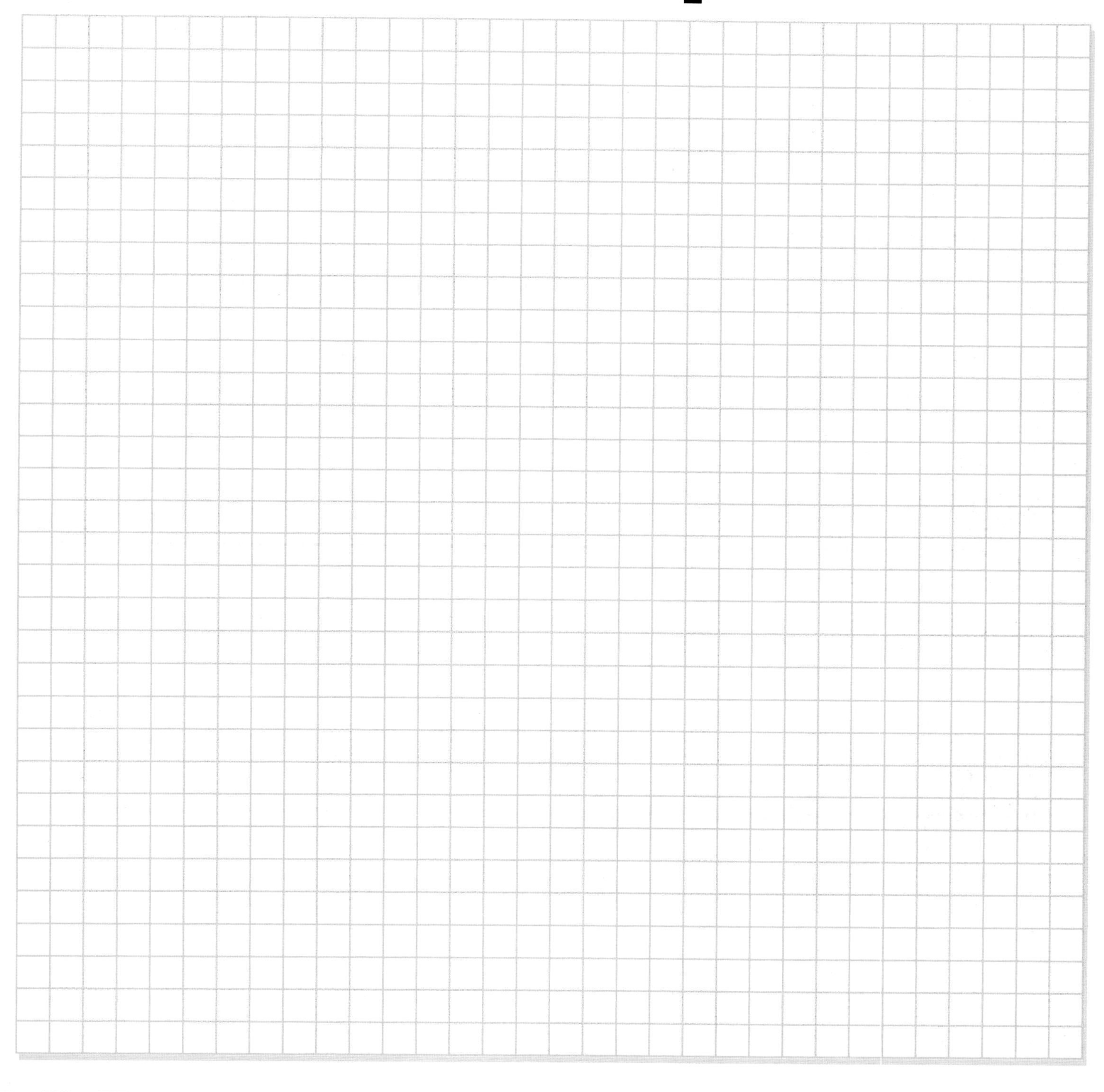

Colorful Cake!

Copy this tasty-looking cake for a brilliant birthday surprise!

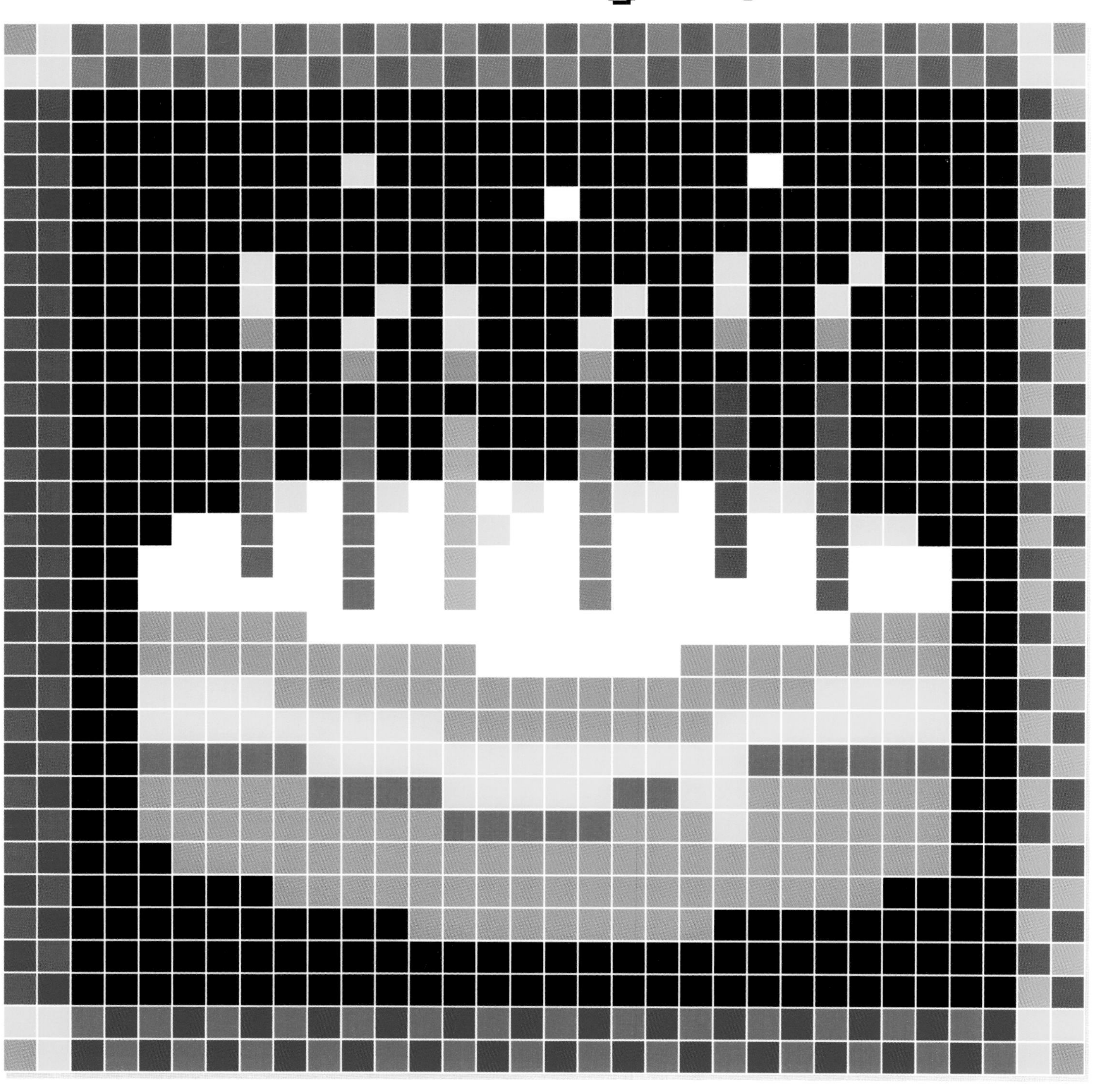

Now it's your turn!

Color in the grid below by copying the picture of the birthday cake on the left!

Amazing Alien!

Be an ace artist and copy this visitor from outer space!

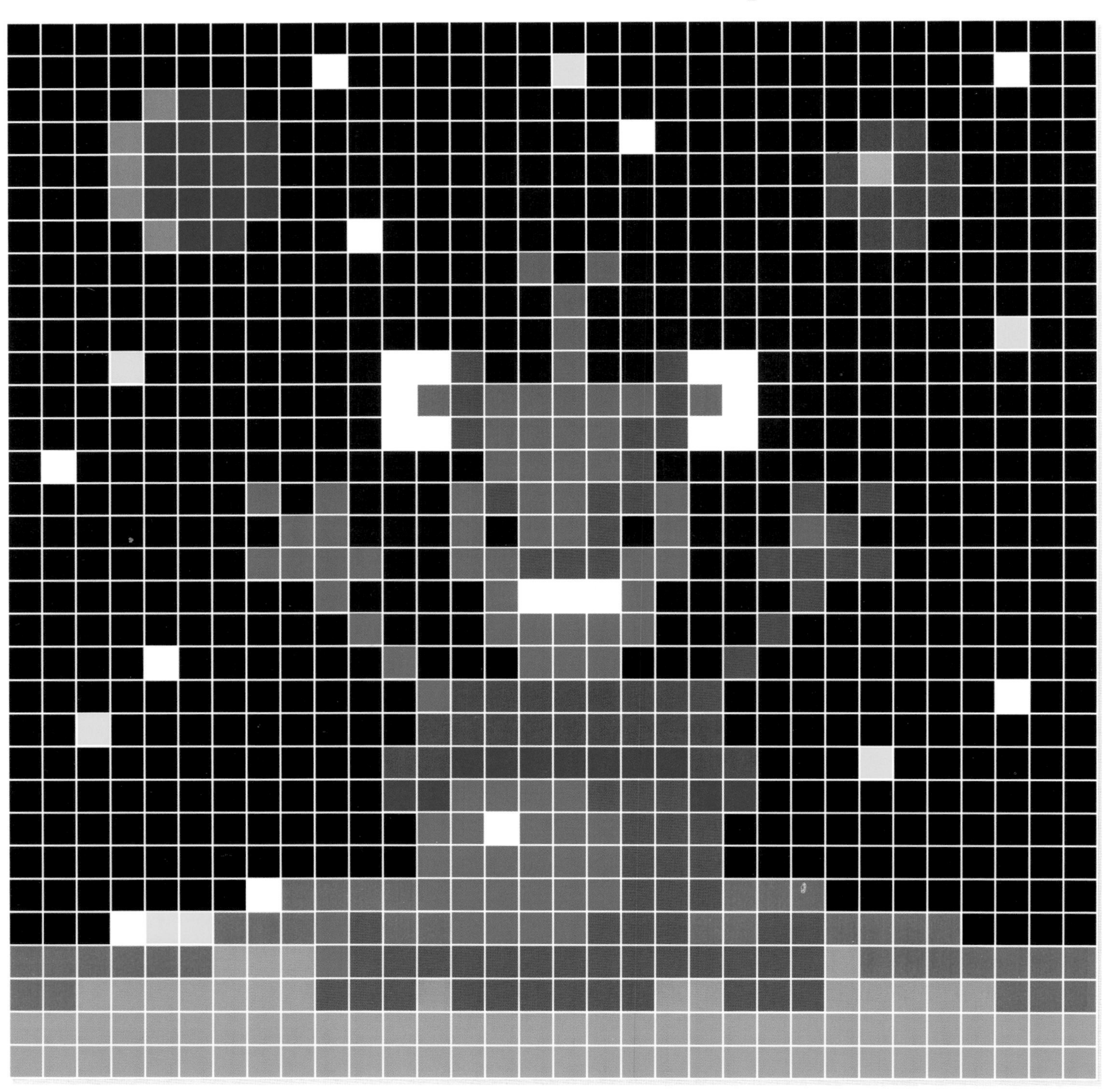

Now it's your turn!

Color in the grid below by copying the picture of the alien on the left!

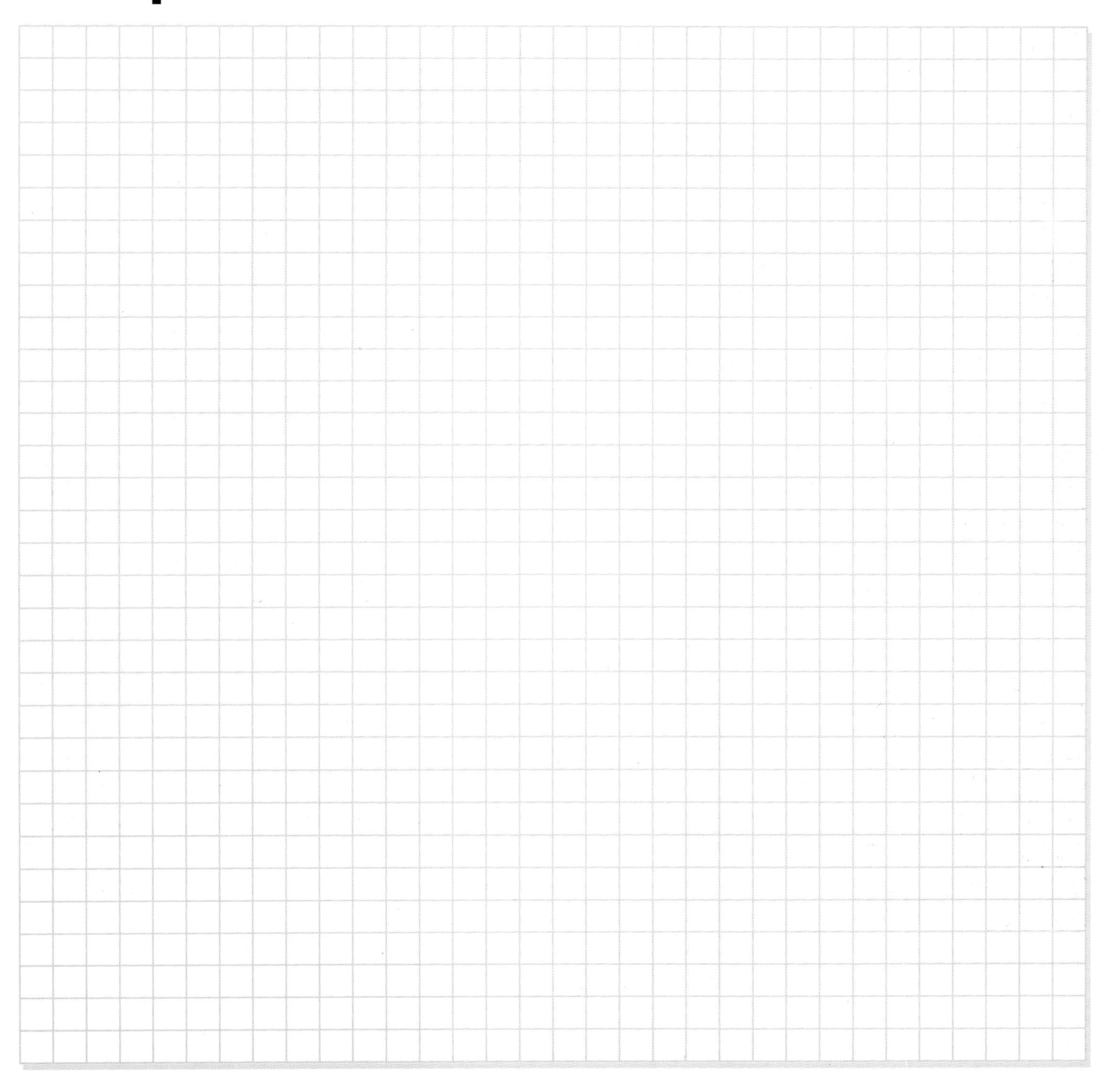

Funky Fruit!

Work your magic and copy this fruity bowlful!

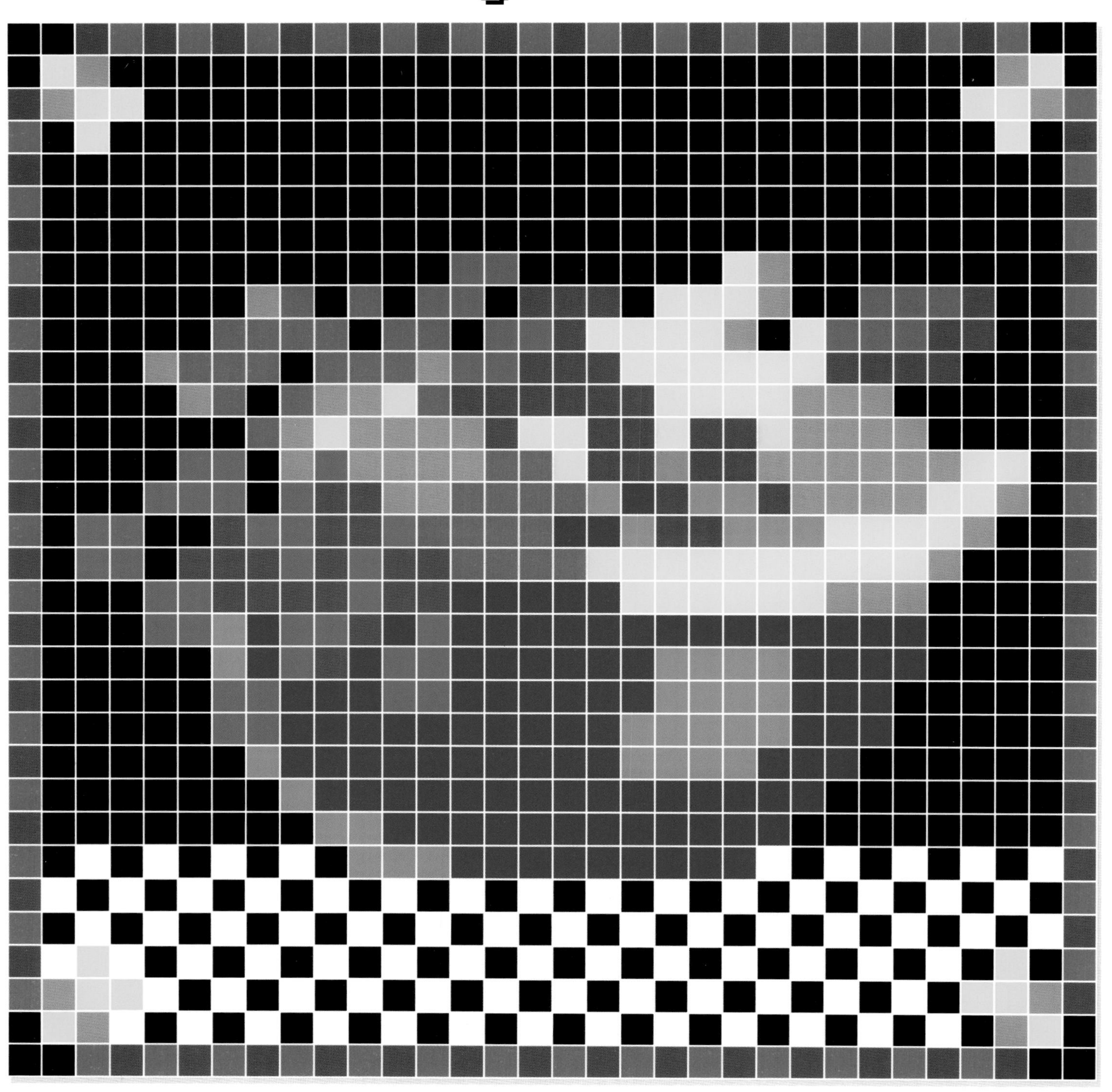

Now it's your turn!

Color in the grid below by copying the picture of the fruit bowl on the left!

Super Spaceman!

Get coloring to create this intrepid explorer!

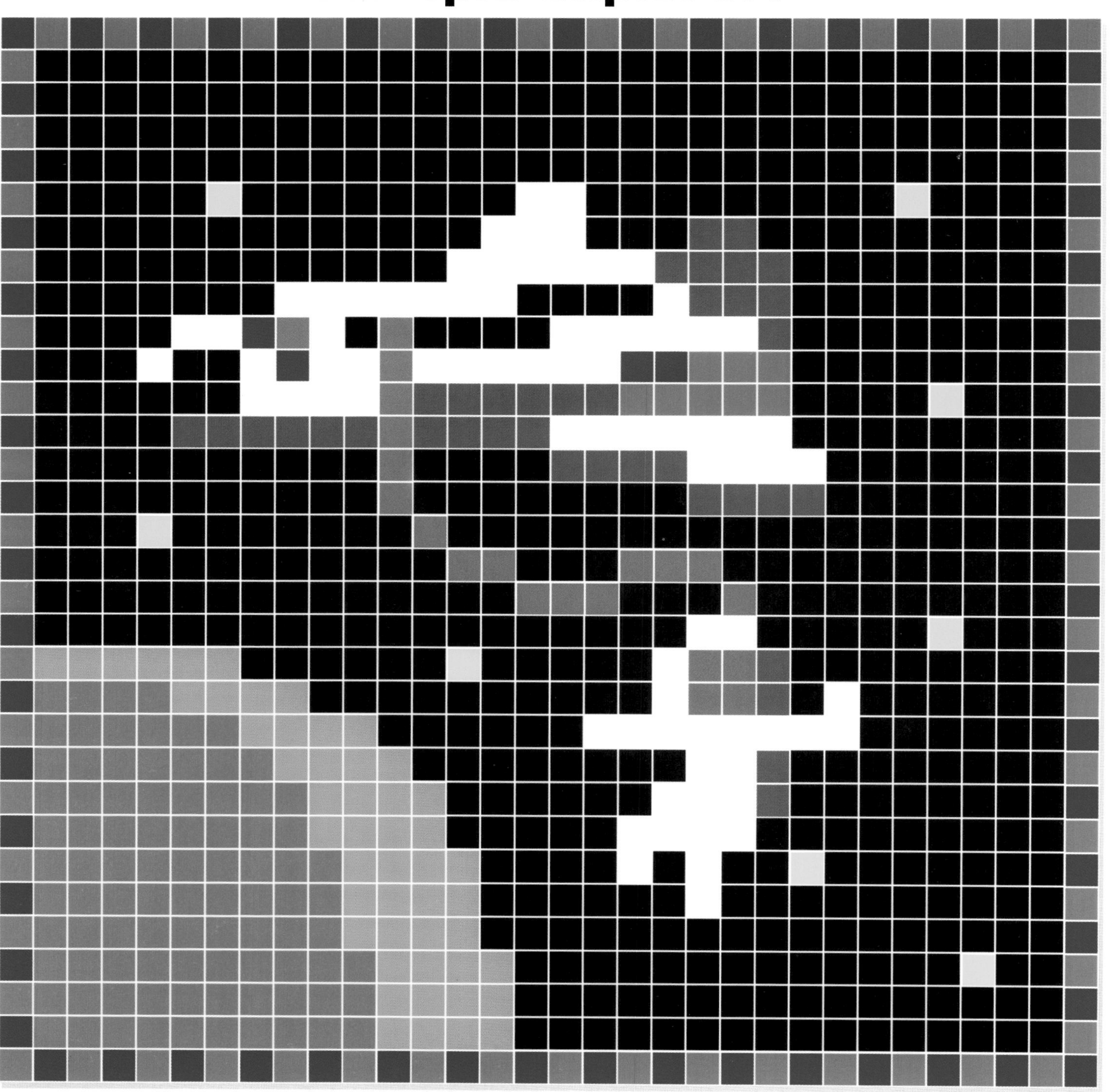

Now it's your turn!

Color in the grid below by copying the picture of the spaceman on the left!

Tropical Treat!

Make a perfect paradise by creating this inviting island!

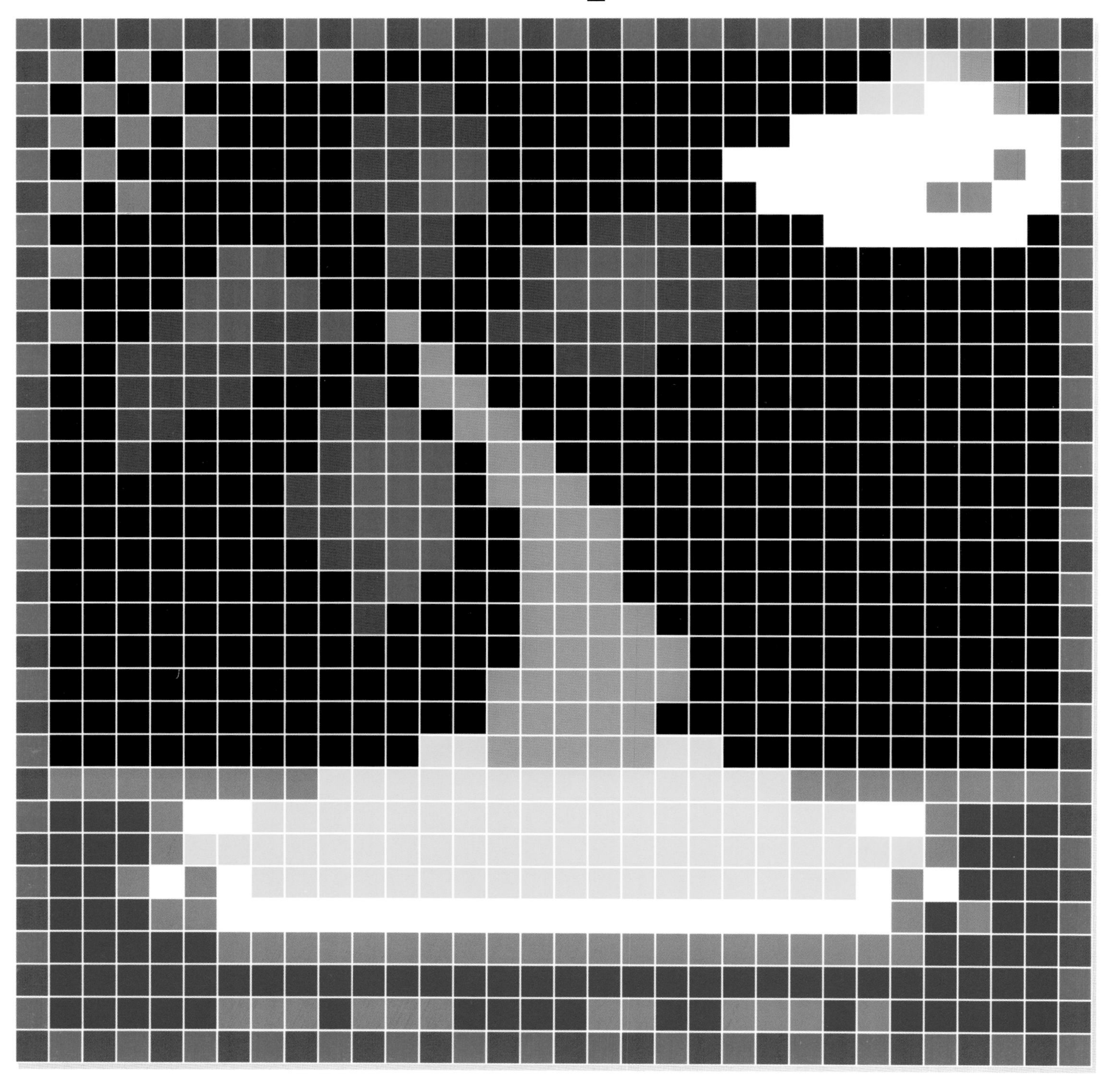

Now it's your turn!

Color in the grid below by copying the picture of the desert island on the left!

Brilliant Butterfly!

Look at the pattern to create this pretty flutterer!

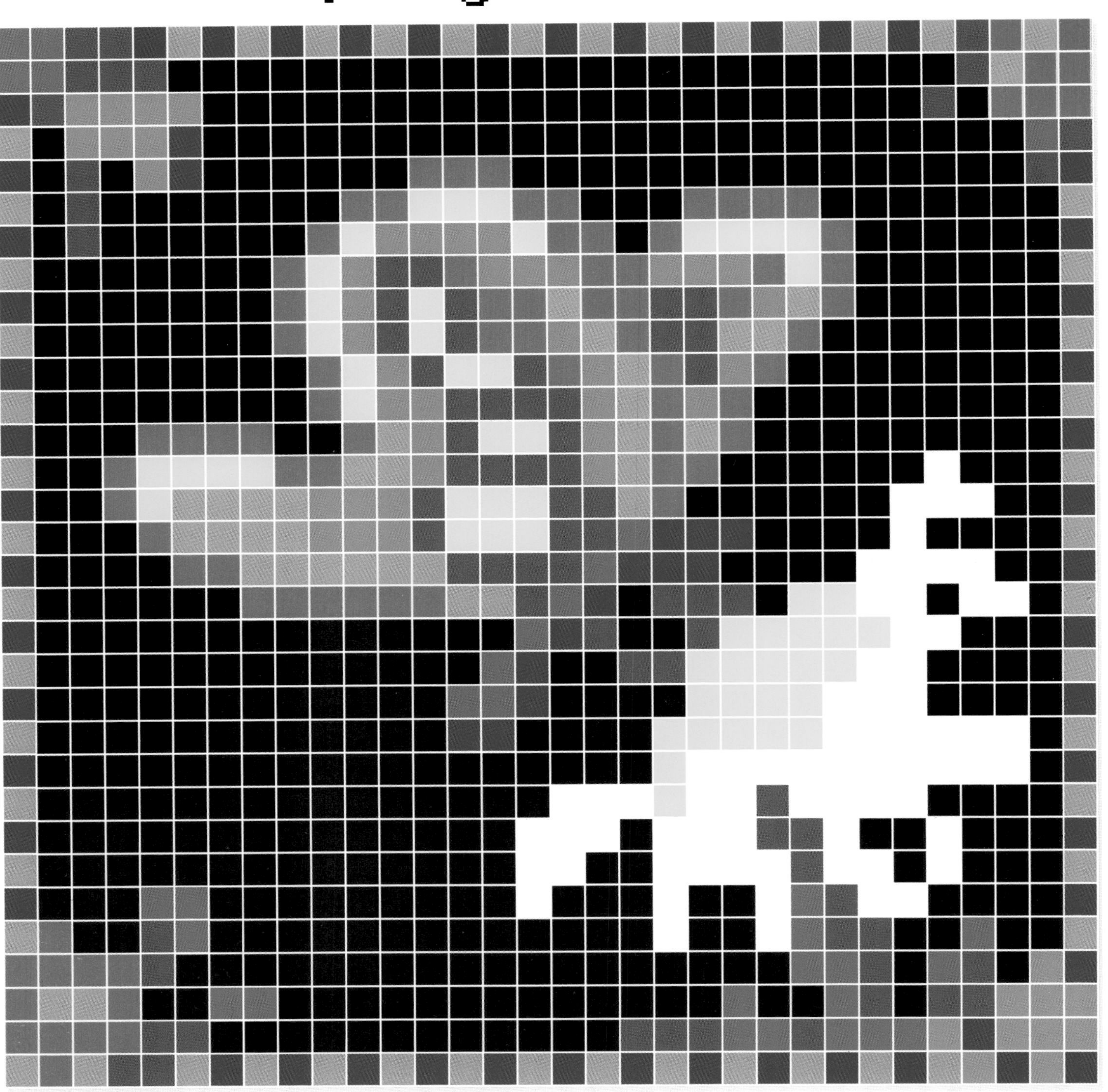

Now it's your turn!

Color in the grid below by copying the picture of the butterfly on the left!

Wonderful Weather!

Copy this colorful picture to create dazzling weather today!

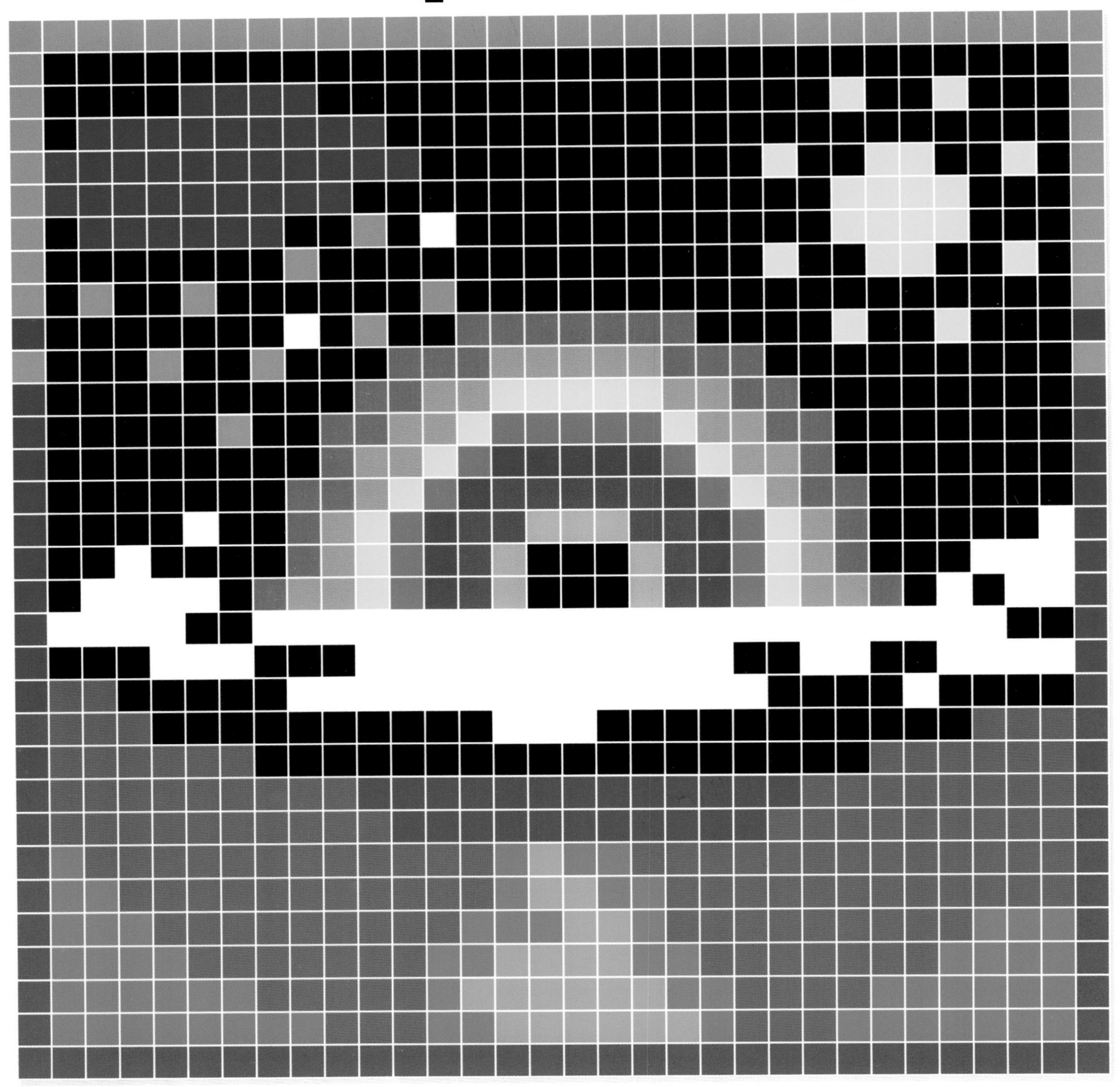

Now it's your turn!

Color in the grid below by copying the picture of the rainbow on the left!

Make Your Own!

Now it's time to make your very own mosaic patterns!

Make Your Own!

Now it's time to make your very own mosaic patterns!

Make Your Own!

Now it's time to make your very own mosaic patterns!

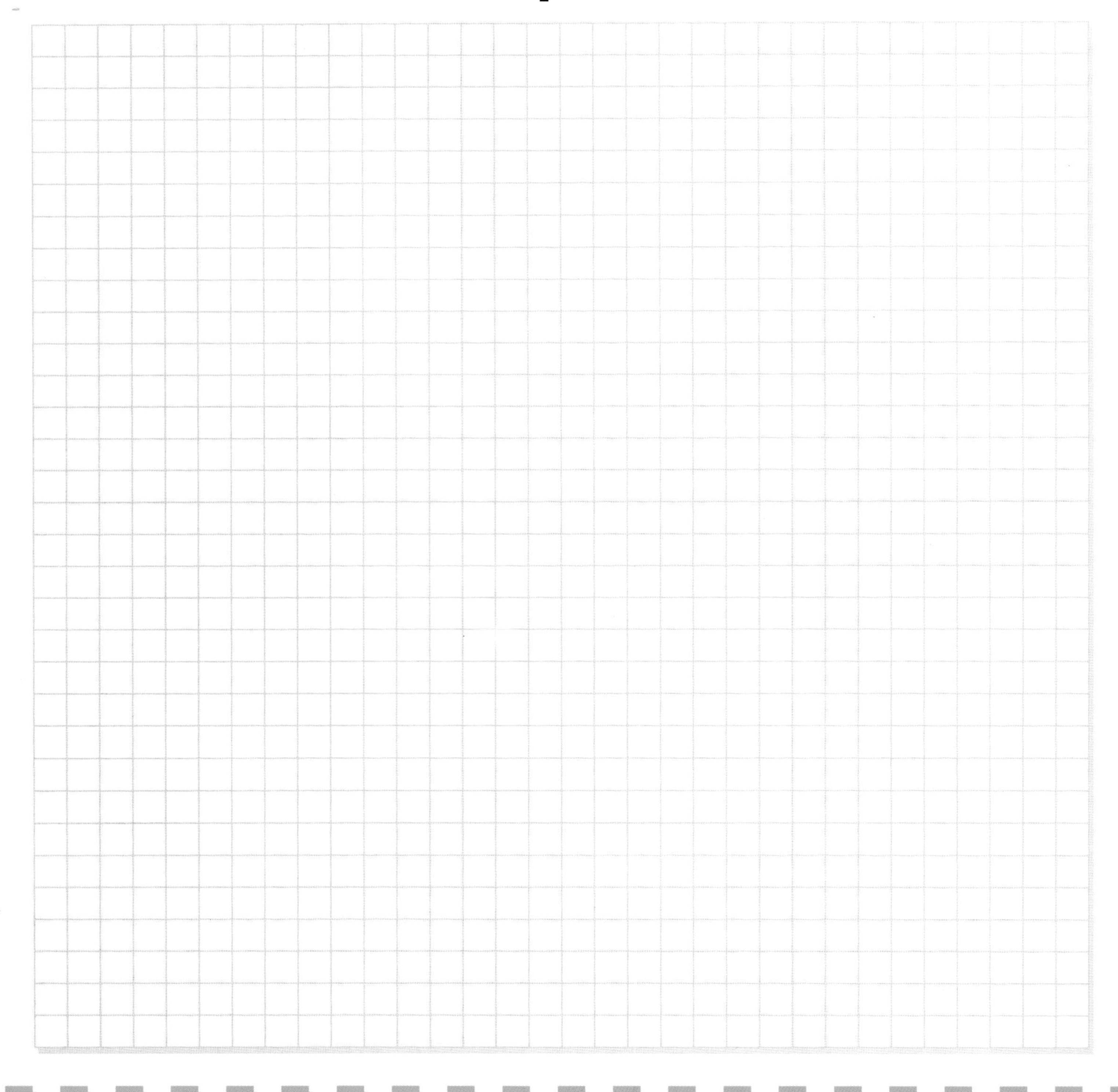